P9-EJJ-514

The Industrial Era

Academic Industries, Inc.
West Haven, Connecticut 06516

ISBN 0-88301-867-5

Published by
Academic Industries,Inc.
The Academic Building
Saw Mill Road
West Haven, Connecticut 06516

Printed in the United States of America

contents

In the last half of the nineteenth century, many changes took place in American life. They resulted mainly from a rapid growth in industry. Railroads and factories spread across the land. How did this happen? Americans had a talent for invention, rich natural resources, and a large supply of workers. All of these added up.

In 1848, there were hard times in Dunfermline, Scotland, where Andrew Carnegie lived with his parents.

The new factory can turn out cloth faster and cheaper than mine. There is no more work for me!

A letter came from Andrew's aunt and uncle who had gone to America.

They write that things are much better there. I think we should go, too!

Yes, I want to go where Andrew and Tom will have a better chance than they have here.

They sold their furniture to get money for their trip.

And what am I bid for this fine loom?

Nobody needs hand looms anymore!

The furniture did not bring enough money. Andrew's mother went to an old friend.

We have a little money saved. Take it!

I'll take it, Ellie! And someday we'll send it back to you!

In Glasgow, they boarded the *Wiscasset*.

She looks like a good, strong ship!

But not large, for all that ocean!

Put your gear in the hold. Below, where the bunks are.

Thank you.

Like most immigrants the Carnegies brought their own food and bedding.

We sleep here. I wonder where we cook.

On deck, I think. I saw a little stove there.

During the seven weeks' voyage, the *Wiscasset* became home. Andrew made friends with the sailors.

The *Wiscasset*'s a fine ship. It was built in Maine for whaling.

Do you still catch whales?

No, no, lad! The ship's been rebuilt to carry immigrants. That's where the money is today.

Am I an jimmigrant?

That you are, along with thousands and millions of others. But America's a big land. There's room for all.

Will there be work for all?

That is a very smart question, lad. I'd say in good times, yes. In bad times, who knows?

In June, the *Wiscasset* entered New York harbor.

Will you be staying in New York?

No, we have relatives in Pittsburgh, Pennsylvania.

'Tis a long trip. Will you go by stagecoach?

No. We go to Albany by steamboat, then west by the Erie Canal.

On the canal boat, they settled down for more weeks of travel.

There are no sails and no steam. What makes the boat go?

Look outside.

A boy led three horses along the path.

We move on the water by horse-power on the land!

For three weeks they travelled across the country.

The sailor was right! America is a big country!

In Allegheny City, across from Pittsburgh, they moved into a shed.

It is very kind of Aunt Hogan to let us live here rent-free.

Son, you've had only four years of school. I wish you could go again.

No, no. I must find a job to help out. We should not have to depend on others.

Finally Andrew's father found a job in a weaving mill.

The pay is not enough to live on. I must help out, too.

She went to a nearby shoemaker.

My father was a master shoemaker, and I learned to bind shoes. Have you any work I can do at home?

Yes, if you can turn out enough work, I can pay you $4.00 a week.

Often until midnight, while the others slept, Margaret Carnegie was busy sewing shoes.

Andrew got a job in the same Pittsburgh mill as his father. They started out together early every morning.

They will pay me $1.20 a week, Father!

It is not much for a twelve-hour day, six days a week.

There was nothing strange about the long hours or the low wages. Workers all over the country did the same. There were no laws about working conditions. There was no social security or insurance. Industry was growing, but so was the number of people who wanted jobs.

Ten years before, Samuel Morse had found a way to send messages quickly over wires. Andrew watched the first telegraph lines come into Pittsburgh.

It's a wonderful invention!

What happens if the wires go down?

No message!

Andrew's Uncle Hogan often played checkers with the manager of the telegraph company.

We need a new messenger at the office. Do you know of a good boy?

My nephew might do.

Send him to me tomorrow. It pays $2.50 a week.

Andrew got the job. Soon he was running all over Pittsburgh carrying messages.

Telegram for you, Mr. Scott!

Thanks, Andy.

He began to come early to the office. He would sweep and clean it before the other workers came in.

Soon his pay was raised to $3.00 a week.

Alone every morning, he listened to the clicking telegraph key. Soon he learned the Morse Code and could send and receive messages himself.

Dot--dot--dash...

Every week he took his pay home to his mother. At last one day she took some money from her drawer.

Go to the post office and buy a money order for Ellie Ferguson. Now we can pay back the money we borrowed!

One day Tom Scott, young head of the Pennsylvania Railroad, made Andrew an offer.

The railroad is putting in its own telegraph. How would you like to work it, and be my helper?

I'd like it very much!

I'm to have $35 a month! And Mr. Scott is often away. I'll have lots of work to do!

You're a fine boy, Andrew!

Railroads were still new, but they were growing fast.

We should have lines running to the West. Back East to New York, too. By canal it takes three weeks!

We need good men on the railroad!

One day Scott had another plan.

I have ten shares of Adams Express Company stock I can sell you. Do you have $500?

I will try to get it.

Mother, is there any way we can raise $500?

We've been buying our little house for $550 and it is almost paid for. I will go to the bank and see if we can borrow on it.

The loan was made. The stock was bought. One day Andrew opened an envelope addressed to him.

A check for $10! One month's dividends from our stock!

So that is how people make money! We've never made a dollar before except through hard work!

By buying stock in the company, we became part owners. They use our money to carry on the business. Then the profits are divided among all the owners.

Instead of having only a few owners, the Adams Company has many. It is called a corporation.

Such corporations with many owners could raise large sums of money. This money was used to start railroads and factories. Soon Andrew Carnegie owned stock in other corporations.

I am very glad to be one of them!

Riding on a train, Andrew met a man named Woodruff.

I understand you're with the railroad. May I talk to you?

Of course. Sit down.

From his bag, Woodruff took out a model.

Yes! I see. Very clever!

I have been working on a sleeping car. It would be used for night train travel.

People are traveling farther and farther! Sleeping cars would be a good idea!

Could you come and talk to Mr. Scott about this?

Any time!

The railroad had two of the new sleeping cars built. Woodruff sold Andrew some stock in the business. The cars were such a success that soon he was making money from this new company.

At this time most railroad bridges were made of wood. As trains grew heavier, there were bad accidents when the bridges could not hold them.

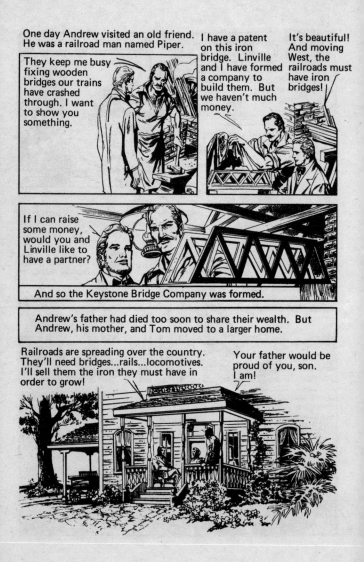

One day Andrew visited an old friend. He was a railroad man named Piper.

They keep me busy fixing wooden bridges our trains have crashed through. I want to show you something.

I have a patent on this iron bridge. Linville and I have formed a company to build them. But we haven't much money.

It's beautiful! And moving West, the railroads must have iron bridges!

If I can raise some money, would you and Linville like to have a partner?

And so the Keystone Bridge Company was formed.

Andrew's father had died too soon to share their wealth. But Andrew, his mother, and Tom moved to a larger home.

Railroads are spreading over the country. They'll need bridges...rails...locomotives. I'll sell them the iron they must have in order to grow!

Your father would be proud of you, son. I am!

In 1859, in Council Bluffs, Iowa, a young surveyor and an Illinois lawyer talked about railroads.

Looks like everybody in the United States is on the move.

It's like that all the way to the Black Hills. I've just come back.

There ought to be a railroad from here all the way to California.

What's your name, young man? In case I run into anyone who wants a railroad built, I'll tell him about you.

I'm Grenville Dodge, sir.

They shook hands, and Dodge watched the lawyer walk away.

He never told me his name. I wonder who he is.

Dodge did not know that he had talked to Abraham Lincoln.

In 1861 Lincoln became president. The Civil War began. But Lincoln did not forget about a railroad to the West.

One of our greatest problems is holding on to the border states...and California.

It would be very bad if any of them joined the South. But we can't spare the soldiers to send to California.

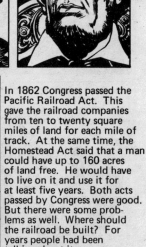

We promised free land to all settlers--and a railroad to California. Loyal men and good transportation would do much to hold the country together.

As you know, Congress is working on a Homestead Act now. But a railroad? We can't pay for a war and a railroad both!

Private companies will build our railroad! We will pay them with what we have--land!

In 1862 Congress passed the Pacific Railroad Act. This gave the railroad companies from ten to twenty square miles of land for each mile of track. At the same time, the Homestead Act said that a man could have up to 160 acres of land free. He would have to live on it and use it for at least five years. Both acts passed by Congress were good. But there were some problems as well. Where should the railroad be built? For years people had been talking about it.

No southern routes --we're at war there. The northern routes are too far north. Find a man named Grenville Dodge and send him to me!

Yes, sir.

Dodge had become an officer in the Union army. He was fighting in Mississippi.

Orders from General Grant, sir.

It says, "Report to the White House at once!" What in the world have I done?

Three days later, Dodge was at the White House.

Oh, it's you! You're the president! I--I beg your pardon, sir.

Sit down, Mr. Dodge. And tell me where we should build that railroad!

It was to be built from the two ends and would meet in the middle. From California, the Central Pacific Company was in charge. On January 8, 1863, a great ceremony was held in Sacramento to mark its beginning.

That's Charles Crocker, speaking. He's in charge of the building.

And that's Leland Stanford behind him, the president of the new company. He is also the new governor of California.

I guess Collis Huntington, vice-president, is still in Washington raising money.

That's Mark Hopkins next to Stanford. He's the treasurer.

Stanford broke ground for the railroad.

This is the first part of the work! And it will continue to the end!

The bridge-building and track-laying started across the plain. In October the first rails and locomotives arrived.

Am I seeing things? Is that a locomotive?

It sure is!

It's for the new railroad. They have to bring everything like that from the East.

That locomotive's sailed 18,000 miles! It has gone all the way around the tip of South America!

Everything made of iron has to come around Cape Horn. That's why we need a cross-country railroad!

Soon trains could run for a short way. But the work went slowly.

There were no steam shovels or other machines. Everything was done with picks and shovels, wheelbarrows and dump carts.

We don't have enough workers, J.H.

It's hard work! The men are always quitting!

I guess you've heard of the big gold and silver strikes in Nevada.

Sure have! I just took this job to get a ride out that way!

At dawn, the Chinese started work.

They've hardly stopped all day!

And look how much work they've done!

They would lift anything, go anywhere. More were sent for at once. Ships went to China to bring more workers. Soon at least 10,000 worked on the railroad. People called them "Crocker's Pets."

Then came the mountains and new problems.

And how do we take a railroad across the Sierras?

Pick-axes, blasting powder, and "Crocker's Pets."

At that time there was no dynamite.

Each keg of powder weighs seventy pounds! How do they do it?

To cut spaces for the tracks to cross steep rock walls, the workers hung from ropes.

Like woodpeckers, they chipped away at the solid rock. They dug fifteen tunnels, each more than 1,000 feet long. Sometimes they cut only eight inches a day. But canyons were filled and bridges were built. Winter brought forty feet of snow. But somehow, with only men and simple tools, the railroad was pushed through.

The Union Pacific Company, building the railroad west from Omaha, got off to a slower start.

In 1866, when Dodge got out of the army and became chief engineer, things really began.

There's no railroad within 200 miles of Omaha. Everything must be brought up the Mississippi and Missouri rivers.

There's scarcely a tree all the way across the plains. Wood must be brought in from other places. And there are the Indians!

Our first job is to send out groups to find the way.

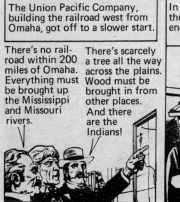

The men worked in small groups far ahead of everyone else.

Sioux warriors attacked them.

Look out! Indians!

Later groups had soldiers to protect them. But the Indians continued to attack.

Red Cloud, a Sioux chief, warned his people.

We must stop this railroad from coming. It will scare away the buffalo. The Indians will have no food!

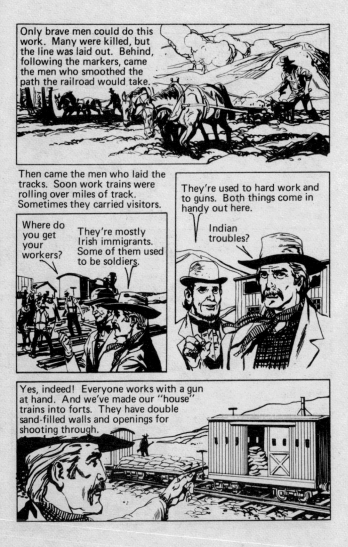

Only brave men could do this work. Many were killed, but the line was laid out. Behind, following the markers, came the men who smoothed the path the railroad would take.

Then came the men who laid the tracks. Soon work trains were rolling over miles of track. Sometimes they carried visitors.

Where do you get your workers?

They're mostly Irish immigrants. Some of them used to be soldiers.

They're used to hard work and to guns. Both things come in handy out here.

Indian troubles?

Yes, indeed! Everyone works with a gun at hand. And we've made our "house" trains into forts. They have double sand-filled walls and openings for shooting through.

The Indians kept attacking. Again and again they had seen it happen: the scouts came first. Then came the settlers. Soon the game was killed and the Indians were pushed off their land. This time they meant to stop it.

Sometimes they tore up pieces of track, and the telegraph lines that ran beside it.

On August 6, 1867, a war party of Cheyennes saw their first train.

It looks like a white man's pipe when he is smoking.

When the train had passed, they went down to look at the track.

The white people have taken all we had and made us poor. We must throw these wagons off the iron road and break them open. Maybe we will find things of value that we could take.

Good! Place the big stick across the track.

They pried up a rail and bent it back.

Good!

At nine o'clock that night, the Indians saw the light of a train coming.

Now we see what happens!

The locomotive and five cars were destroyed. The engineer and the fireman were killed.

Some of the cars caught fire from the burning engine.

Breaking into the boxcars, the Indians found ladies' hats, cloth, tobacco, flour, sugar, coffee, and whiskey.

This happened many times. More men died, both whites and Indians. But still the railroad pushed on.

Nevada has sent a silver spike for the last rail. One of iron, silver, and gold comes from Arizona. But the last spike of solid gold will come from California!

Congress has decided that the two lines will meet at Promontory Point! There will be a great ceremony.

On May 10, 1869, visitors watched as Leland Stanford drove the golden spike into the last tie.

Dr. Durant of the Union Pacific had his turn.

The telegraph flashed the word "Done" to the country. From coast to coast we were joined by a band of rails.

The next morning the first transcontinental train raced past Promontory Point on its way to California. Men from both railroads cheered.

In California, a settler watched the train arrive.

In '49 it took me six months of hardship and danger to get here. I could go back East in six days!

The West and the railroads grew together. If you visited a Texas cattle ranch, you would find that the railroad had made a difference.

How do you do, sir. I'm interested in cattle raising.

I have a few longhorns and a few cowboys. Glad to show you what I can.

Howdy, stranger!

The next morning they rode out across the plains.

Are these all *your* cattle?

These belong to three or four ranches. They've been roaming, and now we're starting the round-up.

32

The cows are branded. We pick out our own brands, and the new calves follow their mothers.

Now the new calf will have the same brand as its mother.

This is my trail-boss. He's about to head out on the long drive to the railroad.

Want to come along?

A cattle drive? That sounds too good to miss!

I don't know about that. It's a long way to Kansas. And dusty, with 4,000 cattle. The herd will be six miles long.

The cattle herd did, indeed, stretch for six miles. The cowboys rode in pairs along each side. Their job was to protect the cattle from straying, from Indians, and from wild animals.

But cattle drives lasted only a few more years. The railroad brought in settlers who fenced in the land and ended the open range. And the railroads kept building lines, until the ranchers needed to travel only a few miles to ship their beef to eastern markets.

The railroads sent men to eastern states to talk the farmers into moving west.

Vermont's pretty rocky country to farm in, isn't it?

Yup.

In Illinois you can plow for miles without hitting a stone. My company will take you there free and sell you land cheap!

That so?

So many farmers left Vermont that farm prices dropped forty percent.

Railroad men went to Europe, too, and the settlers came. Ten years after the railroad was finished, there were almost twelve million more people in the West.

They're going to Kansas, Nebraska, and the Dakotas. How do they know about those places?

On the plains there was no wood, so they built sod houses.

It's cool in summer and warm in winter.

It's nice! Except when it rains, the roof drips a bit into our food.

But sometimes it did not rain for months.

Our wheat has dried up!

35

Tornadoes might destroy everything.

Hail might beat down the crop.

In winter, sudden storms trapped the cattle in high snow.

Many settlers left. But those who lasted and worked hard soon grew wealthy.

They learned that windmills could bring water from deep under the ground.

They learned to plant large fields with grain and to gather it by machine.

They were able to build better homes.

It's a nice house. And the roof doesn't leak!

It was hard work, but it's been worth it!

The price of wheat is very high. I think I'll get some new machines and plant more grain.

Do we have enough money?

I'm sure the bank will give me a loan. This is a good place now.

That's because of all the work you've put into it!

He got his bank loan. He raised more wheat. So did other farmers. Next year, the price was down.

That's the most I can pay. The price is way down. You farmers raised too much wheat this year!

At that price, I can't pay the interest on my loan.

Me neither!

And the railroad has raised the price for shipping it.

They can't do that!

I guess they can. There's no other railroad in the state!

Many of the farmers lost everything, and headed back east again.

IN GOD WE TRUSTED IN KANSAS WE BUSTED

Others got together to fight the railroads and the big companies. One speaker was Mary Lease, the "Kansas Pythoness."

You farmers need to raise less corn and more fuss!

In 1885, Senator S.M. Cullom of Illinois was made chairman of a group to study the railroads.

Our job is to travel through the country. We must talk to railroad men, shippers, farmers--until we know what's going on!

Their report proved that the railroads were not honest. Sometimes they gave people money to tell lies for them. In 1887, Congress passed an act creating the Interstate Commerce Commission. This group had the power to control the rates and practices of wagons and trains crossing state lines.

But the farmers grew poorer while business people grew wealthy. The farmers decided to start their own party.

We must take control of the country. We must bring back the power of the West and South!

We will call it the people's party--the Populists!

Hurrah for the Populists!

People in the East were shocked.

Ignatius Donnelly drew up the party platform.

The government will own the railroads. There will be a fair income tax. We will have an eight-hour day. The number of immigrants will be lowered.

What do you think of that Populist party?

I'm against it!

But in 1892 they got more than a million votes. Within a few years, many of their ideas would become law.

39

When no one wanted the empty land west of the Mississippi, the Indians were moved there. Then came settlers, miners, and railroads. As the white men took over their hunting grounds, the Indians fought back. The army set up posts in the Indian country. Several small wars were fought.

In June, 1876, General Alfred Terry led his soldiers against an Indian tribe in Montana. Colonel George Custer was an officer.

Custer, take your men up Rosebud Creek to the Little Big Horn.

We will divide our soldiers, drive the Indians into the open, and wipe them out!

At once, sir!

In the valley of the Little Big Horn were 2,500 Sioux and Cheyenne braves under Chief Crazy Horse. They swept down upon Custer's men and killed them all.

This was the last real Indian victory. The Sioux under Chief Sitting Bull moved off into Canada.

In Idaho, the peaceful Nez Perce were ordered off their lands.

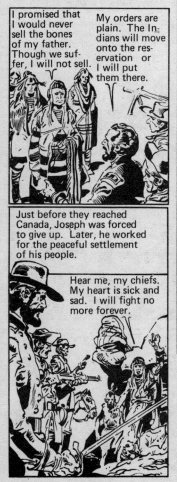

I promised that I would never sell the bones of my father. Though we suffer, I will not sell.

My orders are plain. The Indians will move onto the reservation or I will put them there.

Just before they reached Canada, Joseph was forced to give up. Later, he worked for the peaceful settlement of his people.

Hear me, my chiefs. My heart is sick and sad. I will fight no more forever.

After a failing attack on the U.S. Army, Joseph led his people on a 1,500 mile retreat into Canada.

First the government had tried to keep the Indians on reservations. Then, by the Dawes Act of 1887, they could each be given their own land. The Indians were not ready to accept this, and suffered a great deal. Not until 1924 was a law passed by which all Indians became citizens.

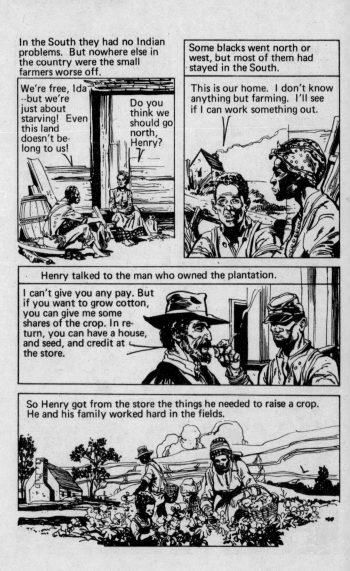

In the South they had no Indian problems. But nowhere else in the country were the small farmers worse off.

We're free, Ida--but we're just about starving! Even this land doesn't belong to us!

Do you think we should go north, Henry?

Some blacks went north or west, but most of them had stayed in the South.

This is our home. I don't know anything but farming. I'll see if I can work something out.

Henry talked to the man who owned the plantation.

I can't give you any pay. But if you want to grow cotton, you can give me some shares of the crop. In return, you can have a house, and seed, and credit at the store.

So Henry got from the store the things he needed to raise a crop. He and his family worked hard in the fields.

At the season's end the crop was sold. The planter settled up with Henry.

It wasn't a very good year, Henry. Your share of the cotton doesn't cover what you owe at the store. But I'll let you pay that back next year.

Is this any better than slavery? I can't even leave, or he can have me arrested!

Oh, Henry! There must be some way we can make things better for the children.

Booker T. Washington was born a slave in Virginia. He tried to give the black children of the South a better chance.

He remembered a day when he was nine years old. A Union soldier had read a paper from the Big House steps.

"...all persons held as slaves... shall be...forever free..."

He moved with his family to West Virginia. More than anything he wanted to go to school. But his pay was needed. He worked first in a salt mine, then in a coal mine. He studied at night by the fire.

One day in the mine he heard men talking about a school in Virginia.

It's Hampton Institute. New England people run it, and negroes can work and study at the same time there.

He saved his money. When he was fifteen years old, with a few dollars in his pocket, he started for Hampton.

Take care of yourself, son.

Don't worry, Mama. I'll ride till my money gives out, then walk the rest of the way.

He was soon walking.

He worked for his meals.

He slept under trees.

When he reached the school, he was hungry, tired, and dirty.

He looks like a tramp, but he seems very interested.

Why don't we give him a chance?

In three years at Hampton he learned all they had to offer. He studied regular school subjects, farming, and crafts.

I would like to become a teacher and help my people.

There is a place for you here at Hampton!

In the little town of Tuskegee, Alabama, a former Confederate soldier, Colonel Foster, talked with Lewis Adams, who had been a slave.

I am running for state senator, Lewis. How can I get the negro vote?

ADAMS HAR... AND TINSMI...

If you will get the government to vote money for the school we need, the negroes will vote for you.

I'll do it!

Foster was elected. The Senate voted $2,000 a year of a school for negro teachers at Tuskegee. Foster and Adams wrote to Hampton Institute, and Booker T. Washington was given the job of running it.

In June, 1881, Booker got off the train in Tuskegee. He walked to Adams' shop.

Mr. Adams? I'm Washington. Where will I find the school?

Glad to see you. But the school ...uh... there isn't any. All we have is money to pay the teachers.

We need a school. And we need you. We want you to start the school. But we'll all help!

The first building was a leaky old church. When it rained, a student held an umbrella over the principal's desk.

Now on page 32...

A small farm was bought with borrowed money. The whole town pitched in to help.

He's old and doesn't see very well. But you're welcome to have him if you can use him.

He's our first animal! Thank you, sir!

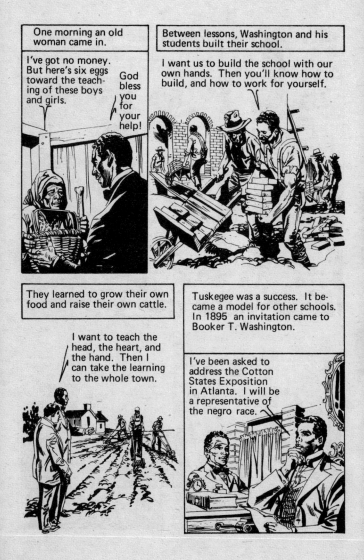

One morning an old woman came in.

I've got no money. But here's six eggs toward the teaching of these boys and girls.

God bless you for your help!

Between lessons, Washington and his students built their school.

I want us to build the school with our own hands. Then you'll know how to build, and how to work for yourself.

They learned to grow their own food and raise their own cattle.

I want to teach the head, the heart, and the hand. Then I can take the learning to the whole town.

Tuskegee was a success. It became a model for other schools. In 1895 an invitation came to Booker T. Washington.

I've been asked to address the Cotton States Exposition in Atlanta. I will be a representative of the negro race.

For a short time, southern negroes had held the right to vote. Then the soldiers were taken away, and the South returned to its old ways. Negroes were no better off than they had been as slaves. In his speech at the Exposition, Washington offered a compromise.

In all things that are social, we can be as separate as the fingers. But in all things necessary for the common good, we should be as united as the hand.

The chance to earn a dollar in a factory...is worth more than the chance to spend a dollar in a theater.

The speech was hailed as great by white newspapers all over the country. Not all blacks agreed.

You are saying we will be second-class citizens!

I am saying we'll put off our demands for equal rights. But in return we want jobs and schools and a decent living!

Yet for many southern blacks, this did not bring the other things.

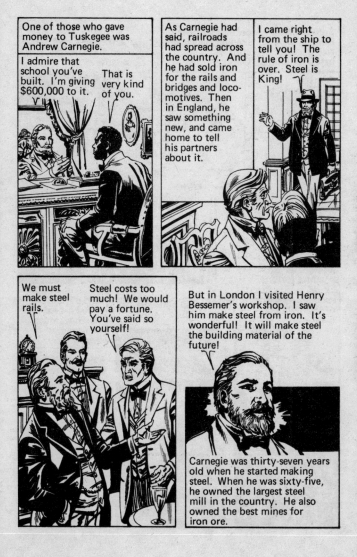

One of those who gave money to Tuskegee was Andrew Carnegie.

I admire that school you've built. I'm giving $600,000 to it.

That is very kind of you.

As Carnegie had said, railroads had spread across the country. And he had sold iron for the rails and bridges and locomotives. Then in England, he saw something new, and came home to tell his partners about it.

I came right from the ship to tell you! The rule of iron is over. Steel is King!

We must make steel rails.

Steel costs too much! We would pay a fortune. You've said so yourself!

But in London I visited Henry Bessemer's workshop. I saw him make steel from iron. It's wonderful! It will make steel the building material of the future!

Carnegie was thirty-seven years old when he started making steel. When he was sixty-five, he owned the largest steel mill in the country. He also owned the best mines for iron ore.

J. Pierpont Morgan, a wealthy man, sent Charles Schwab to Carnegie. He wanted to buy his steel company.

If you'll consider selling, name your price!

Well...perhaps 400 million dollars.

Buying out Carnegie, Morgan joined Carnegie Steel to other companies to form U.S. Steel. This was the first billion-dollar corporation. And Carnegie set out to spend his fortune.

It would go against my honor to die a rich man! I will use my money to help people learn!

He built thousands of free public libraries.

He helped build the Mt. Wilson Observatory.

One day he asked his secretary how much he had given away.

$324,657,399, sir.

Goodness! Where did I ever get all that money?

The use of machines and the growth of factories and cities brought about many changes.

Mr. Benton owned a small shoe factory and a nice home. But Mrs. Benton had a problem.

My dear, something's happened. There's so much more noise and dust and traffic now. I can hardly enjoy the porch anymore.

The town's growing out around us. There are several new factories nearby. The neighborhood is getting bad. Perhaps we should move.

I'm afraid you're right.

They moved too far away for Mr. Benton to walk to the factory. So Mrs. Benton picked him up after work.

Who are all those people? I used to know most of your workers, but I didn't see anyone I know!

I'm afraid even I don't know most of them now. We have hired so many new men!

Many of them are immigrants. They can hardly speak English, and can't read or write.

Can they do the work?

Oh, yes. With the new machines it's simple. They'll work for less pay than more skilled men. You know that my workers cost me a lot of money!

And when times are slow, it's easier to lay off people when I don't know them or their problems.

Yes, I see.

The Benton's daughter, Beth, grew up and went away to an eastern women's college. Home for vacation, she and her mother went shopping.

It's nice having you home. I can't get used to the idea of young ladies going to college! In my day...

Yes, mother ...I know!

That horse-car goes right through our old neighborhood! Wouldn't it be fun to ride down and see how things have changed?

If you like.

But reaching their old street, Mrs. Benton began to wish she had not come.

Why, it's terrible! It's a real slum. And the heat!

Suppose you had to live here all the time?

Slowly the horse-car pushed its way through the people, noises, and smells of the crowded street.

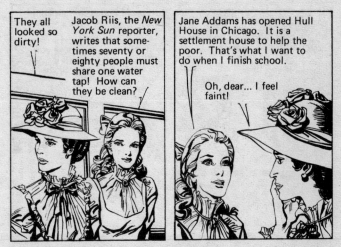

They all looked so dirty!

Jacob Riis, the *New York Sun* reporter, writes that sometimes seventy or eighty people must share one water tap! How can they be clean?

Jane Addams has opened Hull House in Chicago. It is a settlement house to help the poor. That's what I want to do when I finish school.

Oh, dear... I feel faint!

America had become a "billion dollar country," but where was all the money? Something was wrong. Was big business running the government? The worker felt helpless against the companies.

Another pay cut! And we were hardly living on what we made before.

But what can we do? There are plenty of men to take our jobs if we quit.

The old saying goes, "In union there is strength." Maybe labor unions are the answer.

The idea's good! But the unions never seem strong enough to really help.

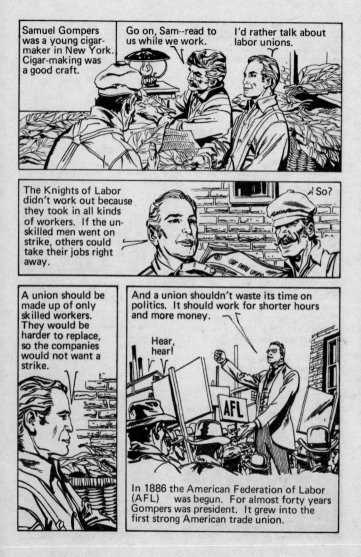

Samuel Gompers was a young cigar-maker in New York. Cigar-making was a good craft.

Go on, Sam--read to us while we work.

I'd rather talk about labor unions.

The Knights of Labor didn't work out because they took in all kinds of workers. If the unskilled men went on strike, others could take their jobs right away.

So?

A union should be made up of only skilled workers. They would be harder to replace, so the companies would not want a strike.

And a union shouldn't waste its time on politics. It should work for shorter hours and more money.

Hear, hear!

AFL

In 1886 the American Federation of Labor (AFL) was begun. For almost forty years Gompers was president. It grew into the first strong American trade union.

As the railroads grew, they came under the control of people interested in profits. They began cutting pay and making men work long hours.

In April, 1863, a group of railroad engineers got together.

We don't have to take these pay cuts! We're important!

They can't run their trains without us!

All in favor of starting a union, say Aye!

We agree that from now on, the Brotherhood of Locomotive Engineers will speak for all of us.

Three cheers for the union!

Other kinds of railroad workers had their own groups.

In the summer of 1877, six railroads announced pay cuts. The workers became angry.

Why don't we stop the trains?

Sure! Don't let them go through!

In two days, at Martinsburg, West Virginia, 1,200 cars were left at the station.

The president, Rutherford B. Hayes, sent soldiers to move the strikers away. Soon the trains began to roll again.

But the idea of strikes spread. At Baltimore, three companies of soldiers fought a battle with a mob of 20,000 strikers.

By the time it was over, thirteen men were dead and a hundred more were wounded.

There were fights in Buffalo, Chicago, Boston, Providence. In Pittsburgh, 10,000 soldiers were sent to help the Pennsylvania Railroad. The first train out of Pittsburgh used soldiers to clear the way.

In two weeks, more than a hundred people died. Five hundred were hurt, and millions of dollars worth of property was destroyed.

Eugene V. Debs, an officer of the Brotherhood of Railroad Firemen, spoke about the fighting.

The strikes were failures! The workers gained nothing. Strikes are not the answer!

Then what can we do?

Each of our unions is interested only in the needs of its own men. They won't stand together! But the railroad owners always work together to put down the workers!

In 1893, Debs started the American Railway Union (ARU).

We will sign up all railroad workers. From the engineers down to the engine wipers, all will work together!

In a year, Debs had signed up 150,000 members. He met with James J. Hill of the Great Northern Railway.

The Great Northern has cut pay three times in less than a year. Without a raise now, the ARU will strike.

Strike, then! You'll get no raise!

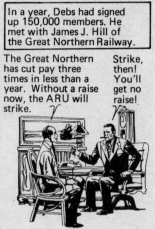

For eighteen days nothing moved on the Great Northern lines except mail.

At last Hill gave in. Pay was raised. It was the first real victory for a railroad union in the United States.

But the next year a strike at the Pullman company was broken. Debs and other leaders were sent to prison. A strike at Carnegie's Homestead steel mill caused a small war, and 3,000 workers lost their jobs. There would be more fighting and many bitter strikes until more peaceful ways were found to settle problems.

★★★★★★★★

COMPLETE LIST OF POCKET CLASSICS AVAILABLE

COMPLETE LIST OF POCKET CLASSICS AVAILABLE
(cont'd)

C47 The Sea Wolf
C48 The Swiss Family Robinson
C49 Billy Budd
C50 Crime and Punishment
C51 Don Quixote
C52 Great Expectations
C53 Heidi
C54 The Iliad
C55 Lord Jim
C56 The Mutiny on Board H.M.S. Bounty
C57 The Odyssey
C58 Oliver Twist
C59 Pride and Prejudice
C60 The Turn of the Screw

SHAKESPEARE

S 1 As You Like It
S 2 Hamlet
S 3 Julius Caesar
S 4 King Lear
S 5 Macbeth
S 6 The Merchant of Venice
S 7 A Midsummer Night's Dream
S 8 Othello
S 9 Romeo and Juliet
S10 The Taming of the Shrew
S11 The Tempest
S12 Twelfth Night

HISTORY

H 1 The New World
H 2 The Fight for Freedom
H 3 The United States Emerges
H 4 Problems of the New Nation
H 5 Americans Move Westward
H 6 Before the Civil War
H 7 The Civil War
H 8 The Industrial Era
H 9 America Becomes a World Power
H10 The Roaring Twenties and the Great Depression
H11 World War II
H12 America Today

BIOGRAPHIES

B 1 Charles Lindbergh
B 2 Amelia Earhart
B 3 Houdini
B 4 Walt Disney
B 5 Davy Crockett
B 6 Daniel Boone
B 7 Elvis Presley
B 8 The Beatles
B 9 Benjamin Franklin
B10 Martin Luther King, Jr.
B11 Abraham Lincoln
B12 Franklin D. Roosevelt
B13 George Washington
B14 Thomas Jefferson
B15 Madame Curie
B16 Albert Einstein
B17 Thomas Edison
B18 Alexander Graham Bell
B19 Vince Lombardi
B20 Pelé
B21 Babe Ruth
B22 Jackie Robinson
B23 Jim Thorpe
B24 Althea Gibson